This igloo book belongs to:

....

igloobooks

Published in 2019
by Igloo Books Ltd
Cottage Farm
Sywell
NN6 0BJ
www.igloobooks.com

1219 003
6 8 10 12 11 9 7
ISBN 978-1-78810-165-3

Written by Melanie Joyce
Illustrated by Daniel Howarth

Cover designed by Alex Alexandrou
Interiors designed by Amy Bradford
Edited by Kathryn Beer

Printed and manufactured in China

Cheer Up, Chicken!

igloobooks

Everyone was busy at Blossom Tree Farmyard,
preparing for the county fair and **working** very hard.

Doris the chicken, however, simply would not lay,
because the naughty fox had been **upsetting** her all day.

"Oh, dear," said the cockerel. "That fox is such a pain. Now Doris will never go to the county fair again."

He told the other animals that Doris was distressed.

"Try to cheer her up," he said.
"Please all do your best."

Oink! went the pigs, **excitedly**.
They formed a pig dance group.

They stood on their trotters in tutus
and **twirled** round the chicken coop.

Doris just **ruffled** her feathers
and gave a sad little sigh.

"*Suit yourself*," said the pigs, **pirouetting** back to their sty.

"**MOO!**"

went Daisy the cow, ZOOMING by in a plane.

She looped-the-loop twice over and swooped by once again.

BAA! went the sheep.

Chocks away!

They did a parachute jump, but landed in the pigsty with a very **squelchy SHLUMP!**

The geese tried ballroom dancing.
The horse dressed up as a clown.

The billy goats started a disco
and everyone **boogied** on down.

Doris hardly noticed Kitty swinging on a trapeze.
"Oh, Doris," said the cockerel.

"Just lay one little
egg for us, please."

Doris didn't move a muscle. There wasn't even a cluck.
The animals all moved closer.

"I'll wake her up!"
said Foxy.
He **leapt** out in a
FLASH...

... but caught his tail
on a pitchfork
and **landed**
with a...

... SPLASH!

At first Doris looked **astonished**, then she looked **amused**...

... to see that fox in the water trough, looking quite **confused**.

Doris flapped her wings and gave a hearty laugh.
"Look everyone," she said.

Foxy took
a bath!

"Hee-hee, ha-ha!" cried Doris,
as she ROLLED around the straw.

Cluck! She laid an egg.
Cluck, cluck! She laid two more.

"Goodbye, Foxy," she said.
"Don't come back anytime soon."

Then, Doris **laughed** so much,
she laid eggs all afternoon.

The animals were happy that Doris had finally laid.

Well Done, Doris!

"Thank you everyone," she said,
"for all the effort you made."

"Thank you, Cockerel," said Doris, settling in her nest.

She roosted on her clutch of eggs and had a lovely rest.

So it was that Doris went to the county fair.
Foxy was forgiven, and even he went there.

County Fair

Doris was so proud, and wanted everyone to know,
that all her farmyard friends helped her win best in show!